Coronavirus and Me:

Lael and Zara's Point of View

Joanna Brown

ISBN: 978-976-8290-23-6
Printed in the United States of America.
Trinity Hills Publishing
www.trinityhillspublishing.com

DEDICATION

This book is dedicated to our precious daughters Lael and Zara Brown for their aptitude and enthusiasm to share their thoughts on this 2020 pandemic. May you both continue to shine and grow in the grace of God. We love you so much.

It was the day before my school's sports and everyone was making a fuss; fixing pompoms, socks, ribbons and stuff.

We were learning to march,
left right! left right!

then Miss told us something that gave us a fright.

5

Coronavirus is in the air,
and she told us not to fear.

When my Mommy came
to pick us up from school,

Miss told the class that
there was a new rule...

She said, "Class, when you get home, please, wash your hands, drink lots of water and eat your veggies.

Oh! and cover your nose when you sneeze, ACHOO!"

Miss showed us a picture of the bug, Wow! It was even stranger than the one I found under the rug.

7

That was the last day I saw my
school, my teachers, my friends
and that swimming pool.

Mommy and Daddy are
home every day,
we all come together and we pray.

For all those who are sick,
we ask Jesus to heal
them quick, quick, quick.

When our parents go out, they can't take us,
because it's so easy to get the Coronavirus.

The thing is, it can be anywhere, That's why
it's important to take good care.

People are keeping their distance
and no longer hugging.

I think they say
it's a "social thing".

My sister and I have masks to put on,
but since we don't go anywhere, we just leave them alone.

I don't have the virus but it has
affected me,
in fact; it has affected everybody.

Those who don't have Coronavirus
knows someone who does,
This bug is sure making a buzz.

All the fun places are now
closed, can't visit the mall, the
play park or any one of those.

10

My Mommy found lots of things for us to do.
we played dress-up, had parties and made ice-cream too.

II

Being at home with Mommy and Daddy is so cool,

but tomorrow when Coronavirus is over, I'm going back to school.

12

ACKNOWLEDGEMENTS

I am eternally grateful to my Lord and Saviour Jesus Christ who has unquestionably given me the ability to compose this content. To my dear husband Curt, thank you for your undying love and support to me in this venture. I must also thank my mother Cheryl and my siblings; Asha-Dee, Zhiggi, Sonja and Marc for their assistance and encouragement. To Mrs. Amber Joy Daniel, thank you for narrating, Mr. Azam Aziz, thanks for the referrals, Mrs. Euline Peters, thank you for your editing suggestions. Ms. Christal Chapman and Mr. Joash Huggins, I appreciate your wise counsel. To the Trinity Hills Publishing Team, thanks for everything. You all have assisted me tremendously in more ways than one. May you be blessed as you read this book with joy.

ABOUT THE AUTHOR

Mrs. Joanna Brown is a believer in the Lord Jesus Christ who ascribes all of her literary abilities to Almighty God. She is the wife of Mr. Curt Brown, and together they have two lovely daughters, Lael and Zara.

A crafter by nature however, Mrs. Brown occasionally composes songs and poetry. She commenced writing content for children after becoming a mother in 2013. It is her heart's desire to see children learn key principles as pertains to life and Godliness, in a simple yet entertaining way. This book, was specifically penned with children in mind, as it was derived from the point of view of her very own children.

NOTES

NOTES

_____

_____

_____

_____

_____

_____

_____

_____

_____

_____

_____

NOTES

_____

_____

_____

_____

_____

_____

_____

_____

_____

_____

_____

CPSIA information can be obtained
at www.ICGtesting.com
Printed in the USA
BVHW021255021221
622875BV00029B/840

9 789768 290236